SPELLING

RULES and PRACTICE 1

Susan J. Daughtrey M.Ed.

Childs World Education Limited
1995

C O N T E N T S

WAYS OF SPELLING THE LONG VOWEL SOUNDS

A B C D E F G H I J K L M N O P Q R S T U V W X Y Z

The alphabet has 26 letters.

Of these, 5 are VOWELS: a   e   i   o   u

The other letters are called CONSONANTS.

There are 21 consonants.

In English, a word never ends in *i*. Instead, *y* takes the place of an *i*.
Sometimes, therefore, *y* may be considered a vowel as it is doing the work of one.

VOWELS

Let us look at the 5 VOWELS. These are very important. If we break up a word into
SYLLABLES, that is, *the parts of a word pronounced as units*, every syllable has a
vowel sound in it. To discover how many syllables there are in a word, it is often a
good idea to clap your hands to the 'beat' of the word as you say it aloud.
Try these:
How many syllables are in:

education?	ed/u/ca/tion	4
cupboard?	cup/board	2
conceal?	con/ceal	2
hippopotamus?	hip/po/pot/am/us	5
hat?	hat	1

and so on. Choose words of your own and practise breaking up words into their
syllables.

Do you notice that each syllable has one vowel sound in it? Underline the vowels in
the words above. *Conceal* has two vowels which make one vowel sound in its last
syllable; so has *cupboard*. In *education*, one of the syllables is a vowel only! So
vowels are very important, and they are in every word, even little words like *sit*,
win, *peg* and so on.

VOWEL SOUNDS

When we read a word, there are two ways a vowel can be sounded. If it says its
SOUND, we say it is a SHORT vowel, and we show this by putting a small cup-
shaped mark above it called a *breve* (˘). These words have *short* vowels in them. Say
them aloud and listen to the sound of the short vowel.

mat beg pin top fun

Now say these words. In these words the vowels are saying their NAME - they
make a LONG vowel sound. We show this by putting a small line above the vowel.

We call the short line a *macron*(-). Say these words aloud and listen to the long vowel sound.

$$\bar{\text{mate}} \quad \bar{\text{bone}} \quad \bar{\text{pine}} \quad \bar{\text{slope}} \quad \bar{\text{fume}}$$

A vowel will always be short and say its sound unless we do something to it. To make a vowel *long* and so say its *name*, we could add a *silent e*, or perhaps put two vowels together which make one sound, such as *ea, ee, ai* and so on. We call this letter pattern a *vowel digraph*. In these cases it is usually the first of the two vowels that makes the sound. A fun way to remember this is to say, 'When two vowels go out walking it is usually the first that does the talking'. We shall come back to these spellings later.

First let us look at short words which have only ONE vowel in them, are ONE syllable long and end in ONE consonant.

We'll call this the ***ONE ONE ONE* RULE**.

These small words follow the *ONE ONE ONE* Rule:

fit   win   set   beg   pot   hit   van   cot   fun   hop

ADDING A SUFFIX

A SUFFIX is a letter or group of letters added to the end of a word which changes its meaning slightly. A suffix may start with a consonant, such as:

-ment   -ly   -ness   -ful

or a vowel, such as:

-ed   -ing   -est   -ish   -en   -y   -er

THE DOUBLING RULE

> **To keep the short sound of a vowel, there are usually TWO CONSONANTS between the short vowel and the next vowel.**

To achieve this we may have to do something to the word. To help you decide, look at the suffix. Does the suffix begin with a vowel? If it does:

1. **We may need to DOUBLE the final consonant before adding a suffix which begins with a vowel.**
Example:

$$\text{hop} + p + \text{ing}$$

If we want to add the suffix *-ing* to the word *hop*, there would not be two consonants between the two vowels *o* and *i* and the second vowel would have the effect of making the sound of the first vowel *long*. Here, it would read *hoping*. We must therefore add another *p* to the end of *hop*. **This has the effect of 'protecting' the first vowel with an extra consonant and so keeping the vowels apart and the first vowel short**. Now we have:

$$\text{hop} + p + \text{ing} = \text{hop}p\text{ing}$$

Now, the *o* maintains its *short* vowel sound.

NOTE:
If the suffix added is *y*, treat it as a vowel and double the final consonant.
Example:

$$\text{sun} + n + \text{y} = \text{sun}n\text{y}$$
$$\text{grit} + t + \text{y} = \text{grit}t\text{y}$$
$$\text{star} + r + \text{y} = \text{star}r\text{y}$$

2. Simply add the suffix if it begins with a consonant.
Example:

$$\text{glad} + \text{ly} = \text{gladly}$$
$$\text{sad} + \text{ness} = \text{sadness}$$
$$\text{ship} + \text{ment} = \text{shipment}$$

When we add the suffix *-ment* to the word *ship* two consonants, *p* and *m*, automatically come together, so there is no need to add another consonant. In *shipment* the *i* maintains its short sound.

3. Do nothing if there are already two consonants following the short vowel in the root word.
Example:

$$\text{bank} + \text{ing} = \text{banking}$$
$$\text{milk} + \text{ed} = \text{milked}$$
$$\text{land} + \text{ing} = \text{landing}$$

In all these words there are already two consonants following the vowel. These two consonants already 'protect' the vowel so it does not matter if the suffix begins with a vowel or a consonant - just add it.

4. Do nothing if there are already two vowels next to each other (a *vowel digraph*) in the root word and the vowel sound is *long*.
Example:

$$\text{sleep} + \text{ing} = \text{sleeping}$$
$$\text{look} + \text{ed} = \text{looked}$$
$$\text{wait} + \text{er} = \text{waiter}$$

In these cases there is no longer a short vowel to protect and so no need to double the final consonant.

PRACTICE : THE *DOUBLING RULE*

To keep a short vowel sound there are usually TWO CONSONANTS between the short vowel and the next vowel. To achieve this:

1. **We may need to DOUBLE the final consonant before adding a suffix which begins with a vowel.**
2. **Simply add the suffix if it begins with a consonant.**
3. **Do nothing if there are already two consonants following the short vowel in the root word, or if there is a vowel digraph making a long vowel sound. In the latter case there is no longer a short vowel to protect.**

To help you decide:

Look at the *root* word. Does it have:
          ONE syllable, ending in ONE consonant, after ONE vowel?
Look at the *suffix* (ending). Does it start with a vowel?

If the answer to both these questions is *YES* - double the last letter of the root word.
If the answer to either of these questions is *NO* - do nothing, just add the suffix.

Exercise One: _____

Add these endings to these words. Some changes may be necessary. Then, copy each word saying aloud each letter as you write it.

neat + est	_____	_____	fat + ness	_____	_____
sip + ing	_____	_____	big + est	_____	_____
mad + ness	_____	_____	peg + ing	_____	_____
dust + y	_____	_____	red + er	_____	_____
grip + ing	_____	_____	flat + est	_____	_____
wit + y	_____	_____	hid + en	_____	_____
meet + ing	_____	_____	rust + y	_____	_____
hot + ly	_____	_____	plan + ing	_____	_____
help + er	_____	_____	jump + ed	_____	_____
pain + ful	_____	_____	risk + y	_____	_____

Exercise Two: _____

Add these endings to these words. Some changes may be necessary. Then copy each word saying aloud each letter as you write it.

grin + ing _____ _____   shut + er _____ _____

bank + ing _____ _____   wait + er _____ _____

sun + y _____ _____   shout + ing _____ _____

rub + ed _____ _____   ship + ment _____ _____

fun + y _____ _____   chip + ing _____ _____

beg + ar _____ _____   bash + ful _____ _____

flop + y _____ _____   milk + ed _____ _____

skin + y _____ _____   good + ness _____ _____

glad + ly _____ _____   trip + ed _____ _____

swim + ing _____ _____   red + ish _____ _____

Exercise Three: _____

Add these endings to these words. Some changes may be necessary. Then copy each word saying aloud each letter as you write it.

drag + ed _____ _____   sleep + ing _____ _____

hard + en _____ _____   jam + ed _____ _____

bad + ly _____ _____   crisp + y _____ _____

slim + ed _____ _____   jag + ed _____ _____

lug + age _____ _____   farm + ing _____ _____

cold + ness _____ _____   star + y _____ _____

fret + ful _____ _____   stab + ed _____ _____

hard + er _____ _____   flop + y _____ _____

wood + en _____ _____   rot + en _____ _____

stop + ing _____ _____   grin + ing _____ _____

In the Exercises above, the final consonant of each ONE syllable word ending in ONE consonant following ONE short vowel was doubled when a vowel suffix was added. In all these words, the stress was on the last (only) syllable before the suffix was added.

In words of *more than one syllable* where the stress is on the last syllable, the DOUBLING RULE applies, that is, the final consonant is doubled before a vowel suffix is added.

Example:

begin becomes beginner and beginning

The last syllable is stressed, the final consonant is doubled.

forget becomes forgotten and forgetting

The last syllable is stressed, the final consonant is doubled.

regret becomes regretted and regretting

The last syllable is stressed, the final consonant is doubled.

There are, however, two points about the **DOUBLING RULE** which apply to *words of more than one syllable* which should be noted:

1. If the *first* syllable of a polysyllabic word is stressed, the final consonant is *not* doubled.

Example:

market	marketing
garden	gardening
offer	offering

2. If, when the vowel suffix is added, the stress changes and is no longer on the last syllable but shifts on to the first syllable, the final consonant is *not* doubled, the suffix is simply added.

Example:

refer	referring	referred	**but**	reference
prefer	preferring	preferred	**but**	preference

Here the *stress* is no longer on the last syllable, but has shifted onto the first syllable. *In these cases the final consonant is **not** doubled.*

These exceptions apply to every spelling EXCEPT those words ending in *l*. In the case of a polysyllabic word that ends in *l* preceded by a single vowel, double the *l* regardless of stress.

Example:

counsel	counselled	counselling	
cancel	cancelled	cancelling	cancellation

Here is an exercise of useful words of more than one syllable that contain a double letter after a short vowel sound. Also listed are some *exceptions*. Always try to learn separately and remember any exceptions to a Rule.

Exercise Four: _____

Copy carefully these words with a short vowel sound putting a circle around the double letters. Look at the letter patterns carefully. When you are ready, cover the word and re-write it from memory.

Words with *ll*:

valley	_____	_____	village	_____	_____
million	_____	_____	illustrate	_____	_____
cellar	_____	_____	gallery	_____	_____
gallop	_____	_____	brilliant	_____	_____
silly	_____	_____	holly	_____	_____
jewellery	_____	_____	collect	_____	_____
collection	_____	_____	recollect	_____	_____

Exceptions include: melon melody volume holiday

Words with *tt*:

attic	_____	_____	butter	_____	_____
butterfly	_____	_____	bitter	_____	_____
better	_____	_____	letter	_____	_____
button	_____	_____	mutton	_____	_____
cotton	_____	_____	attend	_____	_____
attention	_____	_____	attempt	_____	_____
petty	_____	_____	kettle	_____	_____
nettle	_____	_____	bottle	_____	_____
battle	_____	_____	cattle	_____	_____
little	_____	_____	fitted	_____	_____

Exceptions include: petal atom British Britain

Words with *gg*:

foggy	_____	_____	stagger	_____	_____
dagger	_____	_____	beggar	_____	_____
trigger	_____	_____	giggle	_____	_____
struggle	_____	_____	exaggerate	_____	_____
aggressive	_____	_____	juggle	_____	_____

Words with *nn:*

tunnel	_____	_____	funnel	_____	_____

© *1994 Susan J Daughtrey M.Ed.*

kennel	_____ _____	sunny	_____ _____
funny	_____ _____	penny	_____ _____
minnow	_____ _____	beginning	_____ _____
dinner	_____ _____	winner	_____ _____

Exceptions include: canal animal panel linen manage banana

Words with *pp*:

supper	_____ _____	suppose	_____ _____
slipper	_____ _____	slipped	_____ _____
disappear	_____ _____	disappoint	_____ _____
appoint	_____ _____	apparatus	_____ _____

Exceptions include: capital opera depot

Words with *rr*:

horror	_____ _____	terror	_____ _____
error	_____ _____	erratic	_____ _____
terrific	_____ _____	terrible	_____ _____
tomorrow	_____ _____	currant	_____ _____
current	_____ _____	correct	_____ _____
carriage	_____ _____	marriage	_____ _____
irregular	_____ _____	irrelevant	_____ _____
irrigate	_____ _____	irritate	_____ _____

Exceptions include: carol baron garage parade

Words with *dd*:

adder	_____ _____	addition	_____ _____
address	_____ _____	hidden	_____ _____
sudden	_____ _____	muddy	_____ _____
midday	_____ _____	paddle	_____ _____
saddle	_____ _____	puddle	_____ _____
muddle	_____ _____	huddle	_____ _____
cuddle	_____ _____	meddle	_____ _____
middle	_____ _____	fiddle	_____ _____

Exceptions include: madam widow shadow pedal

Words with *cc*:

accident	_____ _____	accuse	_____ _____
account	_____ _____	accept	_____ _____
accurate	_____ _____	access	_____ _____
occupy	_____ _____	success	_____ _____
occur	_____ _____	occasion	_____ _____

Exceptions include: academy

**Words of ONE SYLLABLE
with ONE SHORT VOWEL
ending in -l -s -f and -k sound
end in -ll -ss -ff and -ck**

In these cases then, there is no need to double the final consonant as there are already TWO consonants protecting the short vowel from the effect of any vowel in the suffix. To these words simply add the suffix without changing the root word, whether or not the suffix begins with a consonant or a vowel.
Example:

$$puff + ing = puffing$$
$$dress + ed = dressed$$
$$lock + ing = locking$$
$$tall + ness = tallness$$

**BUT
use -l -f -k at the end of a ONE syllable word
after TWO vowels or one vowel + a consonant**

Example:

$$ban + k + ing = banking$$
$$hur + l + ed = hurled$$
$$mil + k + ed = milked$$

These words already have one short vowel followed by a consonant so it is only necessary to use one -l, -f or -k. Together the two consonants protect the short vowel from the influence of any vowel that may follow.

Example:

$$loo + k + ed = looked$$
$$roo + f + ing = roofing$$
$$fee + l + ing = feeling$$

These words all have two vowels followed by one consonant in the root word.
In all these cases there is no longer a short vowel to protect. The short vowel sound
has now become a *long* vowel sound by the addition of a second vowel (a *vowel
digraph*).

NOTE:
When a word ends in -l, -f, -k or -s sound, there must always be **three letters from
the first vowel to the end of the word** - either:

	1		**2**		**3**
A	vowel	+	vowel	+	l, k or f
B	vowel	+	consonant	+	l, k or f

This is referred to as the ONE, TWO, THREE Rule.

Example:

	123	123	123	123
A	sail	cool	beak	leaf

	123	123	123	123
B	talk	bark	girl	calf

In all these examples there are *three letters from the first vowel to the end of the
word*.

Exceptions include: bus gas yes is has his this us crisis

PRACTICE : THE *123* RULE

-ll -ff -ss -ck
Words of ONE SYLLABLE
with ONE SHORT VOWEL
ending in -l -f -s -k sound
end in -ll -ff -ss -ck

**EXCEPT if there are TWO VOWELS, or ONE VOWEL plus a
CONSONANT in the root word, in which case use -l, -f and -k.**

Exercise Five: _____

Using the *123 RULE* fill in the missing letters in these words. Then copy, saying each letter aloud as you write it.

Fill in -*l* or -*ll*			Fill in -*f* or -*ff*			Fill in -*k* or -*ck*		
foo	___	___	scar	___	___	clo	___	___
we	___	___	sni	___	___	ba	___	___
snai	___	___	proo	___	___	thin	___	___
mea	___	___	cli	___	___	de	___	___
pu	___	___	hoo	___	___	des	___	___
cur	___	___	sel	___	___	jer	___	___
mi	___	___	roo	___	___	lu	___	___
gir	___	___	cal	___	___	par	___	___
poo	___	___	ru	___	___	lea	___	___
fee	___	___	hal	___	___	wre	___	___
snar	___	___	bee	___	___	li	___	___
hur	___	___	mu	___	___	jun	___	___
wi	___	___	stu	___	___	ban	___	___
pai	___	___	lea	___	___	boo	___	___
ta	___	___	sti	___	___	su	___	___
too	___	___	loa	___	___	sli	___	___
tai	___	___	blu	___	___	cra	___	___
ce	___	___	ree	___	___	coo	___	___
hee	___	___	grie	___	___	blea	___	___
du	___	___	aloo	___	___	tan	___	___

Exercise Six: _____

Using the *DOUBLING RULE* and the *123 RULE*, complete these words making any changes that may be necessary. Then copy each word, saying the letters aloud as you do so. All these words have a *short* vowel sound.

sit + ing	_____	_____	snif + ed	_____	_____
dres + ing	_____	_____	park + ed	_____	_____
bark + ing	_____	_____	swim + ing	_____	_____
ship + ment	_____	_____	glad + ly	_____	_____

cros + ing	_____ _____	puf + ing	_____ _____
gues + ed	_____ _____	buz + er	_____ _____
diz + y	_____ _____	pas + age	_____ _____
rub + ish	_____ _____	hid + en	_____ _____
dim + er	_____ _____	fit + ment	_____ _____

Exercise Seven: _____

Using the *DOUBLING RULE* and the *123 RULE*, complete these words, making any changes that may be necessary. Then copy each word, saying the letters aloud as you do so. This time there are words with a *short* vowel sound, and words with a *long* vowel sound (vowel digraph).

cloak + ed	_____ _____	snif + ing	_____ _____
mis + ed	_____ _____	ful + er	_____ _____
fit + ment	_____ _____	kneel + ing	_____ _____
bank + ing	_____ _____	sad + ness	_____ _____
slip + ed	_____ _____	surf + ing	_____ _____
cap + ful	_____ _____	twirl + ed	_____ _____
sweet + er	_____ _____	milk + ing	_____ _____
pat + ed	_____ _____	wrap + ed	_____ _____
mad + ly	_____ _____	sail + ing	_____ _____
sel + ing	_____ _____	spoil + ed	_____ _____
band + age	_____ _____	flat + en	_____ _____

Exercise Eight:_____

Copy carefully these words of two or more syllables which have *ss* in them. Study the letter patterns, and when you are ready, cover over the word and try to write it from memory.

address	_____ _____	actress	_____ _____
embarrass	_____ _____	success	_____ _____
necessary	_____ _____	aggressive	_____ _____
passage	_____ _____	passenger	_____ _____
possess	_____ _____	progress	_____ _____
accessible	_____ _____	distress	_____ _____
harass	_____ _____	confess	_____ _____
process	_____ _____	mistress	_____ _____
lesson	_____ _____	fossil	_____ _____

Exercise Nine: _____

Use each of the following four words in sentences of your own so that the meaning of each word is clear from the way you have used it. A dictionary may help.

      accessible   embarrass   necessary   aggressive

_____

_____

_____

_____

Exercise Ten: _____

Put the eighteen words in Exercise Eight into alphabetical order.

_____

_____

_____

_____

_____

_____

_____

Exercise Eleven: _____

With reference to the words in Exercise Eight, write the correct word next to its meaning below:

a speech to a group of people	_____	great anxiety	_____
a journey by ship	_____	a period of teaching	_____
to trouble or annoy continually	_____	result of achievement	_____
needed, required, essential	_____	to admit	_____
to own	_____	to move forward	_____

THE *SILENT e* RULE

A *long* vowel says its *name*. There are 2 important ways to make a *long* vowel sound. We are going to look at the first of these now. The second method is explained in the section on *Long Vowel Sounds* later in this book.

An *e* at the end of a word makes the vowel say its *name*.

Example:

$$pin + e = pine$$
$$hop + e = hope$$
$$rat + e = rate$$
$$tub + e = tube$$

Say the words aloud and listen carefully to the changing vowel sound.

In all these words the *e* is silent. It does not 'say' anything, it simply has a job to do: to make the first vowel sound *long*. For this reason, it is often known as the *silent e*.

ADDING A SUFFIX:

1. **If we add a suffix which begins with a vowel that can do the job of the silent e, then the e can be removed.**

Example:

tire + ed	=	tir ed
ripe + est	=	rip est
wake + ing	=	wak ing

NOTE:

The **DOUBLING RULE** explained that when we follow a short vowel with two consonants, the consonants have the effect of 'protecting' the short vowel from the influence of another vowel in the suffix. The two consonants 'keep the vowels apart' so the second vowel cannot change the sound of the first vowel.

Here, we WANT the second vowel to change the sound of the first vowel. We WANT the first, short vowel, to be changed into a long-sounding vowel. To do this therefore, we must follow the first vowel with ONE consonant only before a second vowel. The consonants may change but the pattern of the letters must remain the same, so the second vowel will influence the sound of the first.

This is the pattern:

a - *e*   e - *e*   i - *e*   o - *e*   u - *e*

We say *a* consonant *e*, *e* consonant *e*, *i* consonant *e*, *o* consonant *e* and *u* consonant *e*. The dash is taking the place of the consonant.

Any word which fits into this pattern will have a *long* vowel sound. The *e* is silent.

2. **If you are adding a suffix which begins with a consonant, the *silent e* must be kept.**

This second Rule about adding a suffix then, should now make complete sense. If you did not keep the *silent e* when adding a consonant suffix, two consonants would come together. As we have seen, these two consonants would have the effect of keeping the first vowel short.

Example:

wise + ly	=	wise ly
use + ful	=	use ful
nine + ty	=	nine ty
tire + some	=	tire some
care + less	=	care less

In all these cases it is necessary to keep the *silent e* to prevent two consonants coming together and thus creating a short vowel sound.

Example:

care + less   =   careless

If the *silent e* were removed this would become:

car + less   =   carless (without a car!)

PRACTICE : THE *SILENT e* RULE

**An *e* on the end of a word
makes the vowel say its *name***

1. **If you are adding a suffix which begins with a vowel that can do the job of the *silent e*, then the *e* can be removed.**
2. **If, however, you are adding a suffix which begins with a consonant, the *e* must remain.**

Exercise Twelve: _____

Fill in the gap in each of the following words with a *silent e*. Copy the word, saying aloud each letter as you do so. Look carefully at the pattern of the letters. When you are ready, cover the word and try to rewrite it from memory.

These follow the pattern *a - e*:

messag__	_____	_____	damag__	_____	_____
chocolat__	_____	_____	evaporat__	_____	_____
fortunat__	_____	_____	immediat__	_____	_____
separat__	_____	_____	desperat__	_____	_____
surfac__	_____	_____	phas__	_____	_____

These follow the pattern *e - e*:

thes__	_____	_____	conced__	_____	_____
complet__	_____	_____	insincer__	_____	_____
sincer__	_____	_____	compet__	_____	_____
excret__	_____	_____	concret__	_____	_____
secret__	_____	_____	discret__	_____	_____

These follow the pattern *i - e*:

decid__   _____ _____   arriv__   _____ _____

advertis__ _____ _____   recognis__ _____ _____

definit__ _____ _____   excit__   _____ _____

quit__   _____ _____   acquir__   _____ _____

requir__   _____ _____   admir__   _____ _____

These follow the pattern *o - e*:

clos__   _____ _____   disclos__   _____ _____

explod__   _____ _____   erod__   _____ _____

quot__   _____ _____   implod__   _____ _____

ston__   _____ _____   strod__   _____ _____

telephon__ _____ _____   enclos__   _____ _____

These follow the pattern *u - e*:

acut__   _____ _____   rebuk__   _____ _____

consum__   _____ _____   disput__   _____ _____

substitut__ _____ _____   includ__   _____ _____

exclud__   _____ _____   captur__   _____ _____

failur__   _____ _____   figur__   _____ _____

literatur__ _____ _____   secur__   _____ _____

Exercise Thirteen: _____

Add these endings to these words. Some changes may be necessary. Then, copy each word, saying aloud each letter as you write it.

bake + ing   _____ _____   fame + ous   _____ _____

tire + some _____ _____   blame + ed   _____ _____

bone + y   _____ _____   hope + ful   _____ _____

care + ful   _____ _____   wide + er   _____ _____

smoke + y   _____ _____   like + ly   _____ _____

wise + er   _____ _____   like + able _____ _____

bite + ing   _____ _____   tune + less _____ _____

take + ing   _____ _____   spice + y   _____ _____

place + ing _____ _____   shine + y   _____ _____

price + less _____ _____   joke + er   _____ _____

Exercise Fourteen: _____

Add these endings to these words. Some changes may be necessary. Then, copy each word, saying aloud the letters as you write it.

ripe + ness	_____	_____	amaze + ment	_____	_____
write + ing	_____	_____	shame + ful	_____	_____
safe + ty	_____	_____	grave + ly	_____	_____
tape + ed	_____	_____	time + ly	_____	_____
slope + ing	_____	_____	amuse + ment	_____	_____
hide + ing	_____	_____	shade + y	_____	_____
fade + ed	_____	_____	hate + ful	_____	_____
close + ness	_____	_____	smile + ing	_____	_____
grate + ful	_____	_____	laze + y	_____	_____
home + less	_____	_____	rose + y	_____	_____

Exercise Fifteen: _____

Add these endings to these words. Some changes may be necessary. Then, copy each word, saying aloud the letters as you write it.

cute + ness	_____	_____	spite + ful	_____	_____
rate + ed	_____	_____	place + ing	_____	_____
lone + some	_____	_____	advise + able	_____	_____
skate + ing	_____	_____	educate + or	_____	_____
drive + er	_____	_____	grave + ity	_____	_____
quote + ation	_____	_____	blame + less	_____	_____
debate + able	_____	_____	distaste + ful	_____	_____
waste + ful	_____	_____	invite + ation	_____	_____
cute + est	_____	_____	shake + en	_____	_____
tire + some	_____	_____	age + less	_____	_____
hope + ful	_____	_____	shame + less	_____	_____
hate + ful	_____	_____	unite + ing	_____	_____
deserve + ing	_____	_____	refuse + al	_____	_____
pave + ment	_____	_____	use + ful	_____	_____
home + ly	_____	_____	care + less	_____	_____
shape + ly	_____	_____	grime + y	_____	_____

THE *y* RULE

When adding a suffix to a word which ends in *y*
the *y* is always changed to an *i*
EXCEPT

1. When the *y* has a vowel immediately in front of it.
Example:

play + er	=	player
enjoy + ment	=	enjoyment
pray + ing	=	praying
pay + able	=	payable
joy + ous	=	joyous

The *y* remains unchanged if it follows a vowel. It does not matter whether the suffix begins with a vowel or a consonant, the *y* is not affected.*

* The English language is filled with *exceptions* to every Rule. Some of the exceptions here include:

say + ed	=	said
pay + ed	=	paid
day + ly	=	daily
lay + ed	=	laid
gay + ly	=	gaily

2. When the *y* has an *i* immediately following it.
Example:

cry + ing	=	crying
marry + ing	=	marrying
hurry + ing	=	hurrying

In all these cases the suffix begins with an *i*. In English it is unusual to find two *i*'s next to each other. In order then to maintain the sound of two *i*'s, the *y* is kept.

3. Otherwise all words ending in *y* change the *y* to an *i* before adding a suffix.
Example:

heavy + ness	=	heaviness
supply + ed	=	supplied
lazy + ly	=	lazily
envy + ous	=	envious
duty + ful	=	dutiful
merry + ment	=	merriment

This Rule also applies to the spelling of verbs and the plural of a word which ends in *y*. When forming the third person singular of a verb, or the plural of a word, the *y* is changed to an *i* and *es* is added, except as in Rule 1, when there is a vowel immediately preceding the *y*. In that case, to form either the third person of the verb or the plural of a word, simply add *s*.

Example:
We say:

one baby	two babies
one city	two cities
one lady	two ladies

But:

one key	two keys
one toy	two toys
one day	two days

We say:

I cry	he cries
we spy	she spies
they fly	it flies

But:

I say	he says
we pray	she prays
they enjoy	it enjoys

PRACTICE : THE *y* RULE

> **When adding a suffix to a word which ends in *y*,**
> **the *y* is always changed to an *i***
> **EXCEPT:**
> **When the *y* has a vowel immediately in front of it.**
> **When the *y* has an *i* immediately following it.**

Exercise Sixteen: _____

Add these endings to these words. Some changes may be necessary. Then, copy each word saying aloud the letters as you write it.

spy + ing	_____ _____	enjoy + ment	_____ _____
pray + er	_____ _____	multiply + ed	_____ _____
crafty + ness	_____ _____	employ + ment	_____ _____
cry + ing	_____ _____	joy + ful	_____ _____
heavy + ness	_____ _____	glory + ous	_____ _____
buy + er	_____ _____	copy + ing	_____ _____
ready + ness	_____ _____	easy + ly	_____ _____
day + ly	_____ _____	supply + ed	_____ _____

enjoy + able   _____ _____   destroy + ed   _____ _____

noisy + est   _____ _____   worry + ing   _____ _____

melody + ous   _____ _____   envy + ous   _____ _____

steady + ness   _____ _____   pay + ment   _____ _____

carry + ing   _____ _____   annoy + ed   _____ _____

happy + ness   _____ _____   bray + ed   _____ _____

Exercise Seventeen:_____

Take the *suffix* off these words, then write down the *root* word and the *suffix* separately. Remember every *root* word will end in *y* and not *i*. Three have been completed for you.

emptier	__empty + er__	berries	___berry + s__	payment	_pay + ment_
loneliness	_____	employment	_____	smokiness	_____
reliable	_____	joyful	_____	marrying	_____
hurried	_____	crying	_____	keys	_____
worried	_____	happiness	_____	annoyance	_____
mysterious	_____	furious	_____	jolliest	_____
dismayed	_____	dutiful	_____	melodious	_____
daily	_____	heaviness	_____	envious	_____
easily	_____	readiness	_____	craftiness	_____
supplier	_____	enjoyment	_____	happier	_____

WAYS OF SPELLING THE LONG VOWEL SOUNDS

A *long* vowel says its *name*. We have seen already that an *e* on the end of a word which follows the pattern *vowel, consonant, silent e*, makes the first vowel say its name. This is true for all the vowels. Now we shall look at other spelling patterns which make a *long* vowel sound.

THE *LONG a* SOUND

There are three ways of spelling a long *a:*

1. By putting an *e* on the end of a word which follows the pattern *a - e*.
Example:

$$\begin{aligned} \text{hat} + \text{e} &= \text{hate} \\ \text{fat} + \text{e} &= \text{fate} \\ \text{man} + \text{e} &= \text{mane} \end{aligned}$$

2. When *a* is put with another vowel (usually *i*) in the middle of a word, the *a* will be long.

Example:

tr ai n	=	train
p ai l	=	pail
w ai st	=	waist
fr ai l	=	frail
st ai n	=	stain

Remember: 'When two vowels go out walking it is usually the first that does the talking.' Here, then, *ai* says *long a*. When *two vowels put together make one vowel sound*, we call this letter pattern a *vowel digraph*.

3. *Ay* is always found at the end of a word.

In English we never end a word in *i*. We change the *i* to a *y*. If a word therefore ends in a long *a* sound which would be spelt *ai*, the *ai* is changed to *ay*.

Example:

m + ay	=	may
st + ay	=	stay
Sund + ay	=	Sunday
del + ay	=	delay

PRACTICE : THE *LONG a* SOUND

There are three ways of spelling a *long a* sound:

1. Add *e* to the end of a word which follows the pattern *a - e*.
2. Put another vowel (usually *i*) immediately after the *a*.
3. Use *ay* at the end of a word.

Exercise Eighteen: _____

Copy each word saying the letters aloud as you do so. Circle the *long a* spelling.

pail	_____	stay	_____	frail	_____	Sunday	_____
complain	_____	spray	_____	raise	_____	delay	_____
grain	_____	holiday	_____	paint	_____	hay	_____
brain	_____	pray	_____	claim	_____	play	_____
drain	_____	decay	_____	main	_____	today	_____
nail	_____	away	_____	paint	_____	relay	_____

stain _____ Tuesday _____ trail _____ slay _____

sprain _____ Monday _____ chain _____ tray _____

Britain _____ display _____ railway _____ stray _____

again _____ birthday _____ quaint _____ display _____

Exercise Nineteen: _____

Each gap in the words below says *long a*. Copy each word saying the letters aloud as you do so. Study the letter patterns carefully and when you are ready, cover over the word and try to rewrite it from memory.

Put *ai* into these gaps to say *long a*:

barg__n _____ _____   p__nful _____ _____

compl__n _____ _____   tr__ning _____ _____

rem__n _____ _____   tr__n _____ _____

w__ting _____ _____   s__ling _____ _____

Brit__n _____ _____   sn__l _____ _____

p__ntbrush_____ _____   mount__n _____ _____

compl__nt _____ _____   expl__n _____ _____

f__lure _____ _____   w__st _____ _____

afr__d _____ _____   qu__nt _____ _____

Put *ay* into these words to say *long a*:

alw__s _____ _____   tod__ _____ _____

cr__on _____ _____   holid__ _____ _____

displ__ _____ _____   dism__ _____ _____

Making more words:
Change the *br* in *br*ain to ch, dr, gr, m, p, tr and str. Write the new words below.

_____

_____

Change the *f* in *f*aint to p, qu and s. Write the new words below.

_____

_____

Change the *n* in *n*ail to f, r, h, m, j, p, sn and tr. Write the new words below.

_____

_____

Exercise Twenty: _____

Choose the correct spelling from those in brackets to complete the following sentences.

1. The (made, maid) (made, maid) a mess when she spilt the cup of tea.

2. The boy went (pail, pale) when he dropped the (pail, pale) of water on his foot.

3. The (mane, main) feature of a lion is its (main, mane).

4. The (male, mail) delivery service is looking for a young (mail, male) assistant to help with its Christmas deliveries.

5. The little boy was in great (pane, pain) when he cut his finger on the broken window (pain, pane).

6. There are many bargains in the (sail, sale) at the chandlers. I am going to buy the boat with a blue (sale, sail).

Use a dictionary to answer the following questions.
What is a *chandler*?

_____

_____

What is a *homophone*?

_____

_____

Exercise Twenty-One: _____

Put *a-e*, *ai* or *ay* into these words. Each gap says *long a*. When you have finished, mark the Exercise and then copy each word saying aloud the letters as you do so. Cover over these words and try to rewrite each word from memory.

r__lw__	_____	_____	sl__t__	_____	_____
p__l	_____	_____	sl__	_____	_____
gr__n	_____	_____	tod__	_____	_____
mount__n	_____	_____	expl__n	_____	_____
mist__k__	_____	_____	tr__n	_____	_____
birthd__	_____	_____	Brit__n	_____	_____

sn__l   _____ _____   p__nt   _____ _____

tr__   _____ _____   cl__m   _____ _____

displ____   _____ _____   holid__   _____ _____

sk__t__   _____ _____   man_g_   _____ _____

ADDING A SUFFIX TO A *LONG a* SPELLING

When adding a suffix to a *long a* spelling spelt with a *silent e*, remember to :

1. Remove the *silent e* if the suffix begins with a vowel that can do the job of the *e*.

Example:

$$\begin{array}{rcl}
\text{skate + ing} & = & \text{skating} \\
\text{make + er} & = & \text{maker} \\
\text{mistake + ing} & = & \text{mistaking}
\end{array}$$

2. Keep the *silent e* when you add a suffix which begins with a consonant.

Example:

$$\begin{array}{rcl}
\text{state + ment} & = & \text{statement} \\
\text{manage + ment} & = & \text{management} \\
\text{fortunate + ly} & = & \text{fortunately}
\end{array}$$

When adding a suffix to a word with a *long a* spelling, spelt with an *ai* or *ay*:

3. Simply add it regardless of whether it begins with a vowel or consonant.

Example:

$$\begin{array}{rcl}
\text{delay + ed} & = & \text{delayed} \\
\text{stain + less} & = & \text{stainless} \\
\text{pay + ment} & = & \text{payment}
\end{array}$$

Exercise Twenty-Two: _____

Complete the following *word sums* making any spelling alterations that may be necessary. When you have finished, mark the Exercise and then copy each word saying aloud the letters as you do so. Cover over each word and try to write it from memory.

display + ed   = _____ _____   strain + ing   = _____ _____

manage + ment = _____ _____   mistake + ing   = _____ _____

paint + brush   = _____ _____   explain + ing   = _____ _____

trace + ing   = _____ _____   crayon + ing   = _____ _____

dismay + ed   = _____ _____   skate + ing   = _____ _____

THE *LONG i* SOUND

There are 3 ways of spelling the *long i* sound:

1. By putting an *e* on the end of the word which follows the pattern *i - e*.
Example:

$$pip + e \quad = \quad pipe$$
$$win + e \quad = \quad wine$$
$$slid + e \quad = \quad slide$$

2. When *i* is followed by *gh*, the *i* will be long.
Example:

$$hi + gh \quad = \quad high$$
$$li + gh\ t \quad = \quad light$$
$$bri + gh\ t \quad = \quad bright$$

3. In English we never end a word in *i*. We change the *i* to a *y* or *ie*. *Y* or *ie*, therefore, are found at the end of a word which ends in a *long i* sound *.
Example:

$$fl + y \quad = \quad fly$$
$$tr + y \quad = \quad try$$
$$l + ie \quad = \quad lie$$
$$t + ie \quad = \quad tie$$

* NOTE:
A *y* at the end of a word may also be sounded *short i*.
Example:

$$cherr + y \quad = \quad cherry$$
$$berr + y \quad = \quad berry$$
$$merr + y \quad = \quad merry$$

Explanation:
When we pronounce a word of more than one syllable, we *stress* one of the syllables more than another. If the *y* on the end of a word is in the stressed syllable, the *i* usually has a *long* vowel sound.
Example:

Ju ly′

com ply′

sat is fy′

sup ply′

If the *y* is in the weakly stressed syllable, it usually has a *short* vowel sound.
Example:

cher′ ry

fer′ ry

mer′ ry

mem′ ory

his′ tory

ADDING A SUFFIX TO A *LONG i* SPELLING

A suffix can be added to any of these *long i* spellings but remember:

1. To remove the *silent e* if a vowel suffix is added that can do the job if the *e*.
Example:

$$wine + ing \quad = \quad wining$$
$$slide + ing \quad = \quad sliding$$

2. The *y* remains if the suffix begins with another *i*.
Example:

$$cry + ing \quad = \quad crying$$
$$fly + ing \quad = \quad flying$$

BUT when any other suffix is added, the *y* must follow the *y* rule and change to *i*.
Example:

$$spy + ed \quad = \quad spied$$
$$cry + ed \quad = \quad cried$$
$$supply + er \quad = \quad supplier$$

3. Words ending in *ie*, remove the *e* and add the suffix, EXCEPT when a vowel suffix begins with *i*, in which case change the *ie* to *y* and treat as a *y* ending.
Example:

	tie + ed	=	tied
but	tie + ing	=	tying
	die + ed	=	died
but	die + ing	=	dying
	lie + ed	=	lied
but	lie + ing	=	lying

PRACTICE : THE *LONG i* SOUND

There are three ways of spelling a *long i* sound:

1. Add *e* to the end of a word which follows the pattern *i - e*.
2. When *i* is followed by *gh*, the *i* will be long.
3. Use *y* or *ie* at the end of a word.

Exercise Twenty-Three: _____

Copy each word saying aloud the letters as you do so. Put a circle around the *long i* spelling in these words.

might _____ tight _____ light _____ tighten _____

lighthouse _____ sigh _____ delight _____ sight _____

fight _____ slight _____ flight _____ right _____

fright _____ bright _____ night _____ high _____

tonight _____ highest _____ nightmare _____ knight _____

Exercise Twenty-Four: _____

Put *i - e*, *igh*, *y* or *ie* into these words so the *i* is *long*. Each gap says *long i*. When you have finished, mark the Exercise and copy each word carefully saying aloud each letter as you do so. Cover over each word and try to rewrite it from memory.

pl__t _____ _____   w__n__ _____ _____

fr__t _____ _____   l__d _____ _____

surpr__s_ _____ _____   dr__ing _____ _____

l__ing _____ _____   n__tmare _____ _____

kn__t _____ _____   t__ten _____ _____

sl__tly _____ _____   fr__ing _____ _____

dr__er _____ _____   tr__ed _____ _____

fr__tened _____ _____   t__ed _____ _____

sh__ly _____ _____   d__ing _____ _____

Exercise Twenty-Five: _____

Adding more than one suffix. Build a word by adding more than one suffix to a word. Just keep adding suffix to suffix.

start with	*fright*
add	*en*
then add	*ing*

Write one sentence with this final word in it.

_____

start with   *tight*
add   *en*
then add   *ing*
Write one sentence with this word in it.

_____

Making more words.
Change the *f* in *fight* to l, bl, kn, sl, pl and fr.

_____

Use the word *blight* in a sentence of your own so the meaning of the word is clear from the way you have used it. A dictionary may help.

_____

Exercise Twenty-Six: _____

Choose the correct word from those in brackets to complete the following sentences.

1. He (side, sighed) with relief as the train came into (site, sight).
2. The cat clawed with all its (mite, might) to catch the (might, mite).
3. The (sighs, size) of the cake made everyone cheer with (egsightment, excitement, excitment).
4. The (spie, spy) (tried, tryed) to (flie, fly) with his (tie, ty, tigh) in the (skie, skigh, sky).
5. The (site, sight) of the (brite, bright) (kight, kite) in the (nite, night) (skie, sky) (delited, delighted) the children.

Write sentences of your own to explain the difference between the following *long i* words. Make sure the meaning of each word is clear from the way you have used it.

stile and style_____

_____

_____

die and dye _____

_____

_____

right and rite _____

_____

_____

THE *LONG o* SOUND

There are 3 ways of spelling the *long o* sound:

1. By putting an *e* on the end of the word which follows the pattern *o - e*.
Example:

hop + e	=	hope
slop + e	=	slope
rob + e	=	robe

2. When *o* is followed by another vowel (usually *a*), the *o* will be long. (A *vowel digraph*.)

Example:

b oa t	=	boat
s oa p	=	soap
m oa t	=	moat

3. At the end of a word the *long o* sound is spelt *ow** or *oe*.

Example:

t + oe	=	toe
d + oe	=	doe
f + oe	=	foe
gr + ow	=	grow
elb + ow	=	elbow

* *ow* at the end of a word can also be pronounced *ow* as in *cow*, *town*, *vow*. To avoid confusion, I shall only include *ow* spellings which make a *long o* sound in this section.

ADDING A SUFFIX TO A *LONG o* SPELLING

A suffix can be added to any of these *long o* spellings without any spelling alteration, EXCEPT :

1. Remove the *e* from the *o - e* and the *oe* spelling if a vowel suffix is added that can do the job of the *e*.

However, the *e* is kept in the *oe* spelling if the suffix begins with *i*. This avoids creating an *oi* spelling which says *oy* as in b*oy*, t*oy* and pl*oy*.

Example:

hoe + ed	=	hoed	but	hoe + ing	=	hoeing
woe + ed	=	woed	but	woe + ing	=	woeing
hope + ed	=	hoped	and	hope + ing	=	hoping
mope + ed	=	moped	and	mope + ing	=	moping

PRACTICE : THE *LONG o* SOUND

There are three ways of spelling the *long o* sound:

1. Add *e* to the end of a word which follows the pattern *o - e*.
2. When *o* is followed by another vowel, usually *a*, the *o* will be *long*.
3. Use *ow* or *oe* at the end of a word.

Exercise Twenty-Seven:_____

Copy each word saying aloud the letters as you do so. Put a circle around the *long o* spelling.

coast _____   oak _____   boast _____   load _____

toast _____   road _____   roast _____   toad _____

soak _____   foal _____   cloak _____   coal _____

boat _____   goal _____   float _____   throat _____

poach _____   loaf _____   coach _____   soap _____

Exercise Twenty-Eight: _____

Copy each word saying aloud the letters as you do so. Put a circle around the *long o* spelling.

hollow _____   shallow _____   follow _____   sparrow_____

arrow _____   shadow _____   sorrow _____   pillow _____

swallow_____   mellow _____   throw _____   yellow _____

toe _____   whole _____   hoe _____   wrote _____

roe _____   drove _____   woe _____   stove _____

Exercise Twenty-Nine: _____

Put *o - e, oa, oe* or *ow* into these words so the *o* sound is *long*. Each gap says *long o*. When you have finished, mark the Exercise and copy each word carefully saying aloud each letter as you do so. Then cover over each word and try to rewrite it from memory.

l__f _____ _____   sl__p__ _____ _____

s__p _____ _____   elb__ _____ _____

kn__ _____ _____   c__l _____ _____

thr__t _____ _____   sn__ _____ _____

thr__ _____ _____   foll__ _____ _____

h__p__ _____ _____   h__ing _____ _____

narr__ _____ _____   g__t _____ _____

afl__t _____ _____   b__ed _____ _____

fell__ _____ _____   arr__ _____ _____

Exercise Thirty: _____

Unjumble the letters in italics to make a word which completes these *analogies*.

     1. Knee is to leg as *lwebo* is to arm.   4. In is to out as above is to *lwebo*.
     2. *Aotb* is to sea as car is to *aodr*.   5. Black is to *aolc* as white is to *nows*.
     3. *Ream* is to *lofa* as cow is to calf.   6. *Ltal* is to short as quick is to *wols*.

Make up two *analogies* of your own using a *long o* sound.

_____

_____

Exercise Thirty-One: _____

In each of the following questions you must change one letter in the top word to make a new sensible word. By changing a different letter in this new word it is possible to make the bottom word, which is given. Write the sensible word on the line provided.

Example:
Change *COAL* to *BOAT*. Which word would be in the middle?

       C O A L
       <u>C O A *T*</u>   Answer: *C O A T*
       B O A T

Now try these:

1.	K N O W	2.	G R O W	3.	P O S E	4.	R O D E
	S L O W		S L O W		S O L E		H O S E

5.	C O A L	6.	C O P E	7.	S N O W	8.	R O D E
	B O A T		H O S E		B L O W		V O L E

Exercise Thirty-Two: _____

The meanings of some *long o* words are given below. Use your dictionary to find the correct word.

To wet through	_____	Grilled bread	_____
A British tree	_____	A cork does this on water	_____
We use this to wash ourselves	_____	A black mineral used as fuel	_____
We do this to meat	_____	To brag, show off	_____
A football target	_____	A baby horse	_____
Part of your neck	_____	A joint in your arm	_____

Exercise Thirty-Three: _____

In a sentence of your own, explain the difference between the following *homophones*. A *homophone* is a word which sounds the same as another but which has a different meaning and usually has a different spelling.

road and rowed _____

_____

rote and wrote _____

_____

toe and tow _____

_____

THE *LONG u* SOUND

There are two sounds a *long u* can make:

u as in tune, fuse, few, mute

oo as in rule, mule, stool, blue

There are three ways of spelling the *long u* sound:

1. By putting an *e* on the end of a word which follows the pattern *u - e*.
Example:

tun + e	=	tune
cub + e	=	cube
rul + e	=	rule

2. In the middle of a word, the *long u* sound can be made by putting the two vowels *oo* or *ou* together.
Example:

m oo n	=	moon
sh oo t	=	shoot
sch oo l	=	school
s ou p	=	soup
c ou pon	=	coupon
gr ou p	=	group

***ui* in the middle of a word can also say *long u*:**
Example:

cr *ui* se	=	cruise
br *ui* se	=	bruise

However, *ui* can also say *short i*. Take care!
Example:

b *ui* lding	=	building
g *ui* lty	=	guilty

To avoid confusion I shall only use *ui* spellings which make a *long u* sound for the purposes of these Exercises.

3. At the end of a word *ew* or *ue* makes a *long u* sound.
Example:

bl ue	=	blue
arg ue	=	argue
st ew	=	stew
thr ew	=	threw

The *ue* spelling is generally found at the end of a word of more than one syllable.
Example:

tiss ue	=	tissue
resc ue	=	rescue

ADDING A SUFFIX TO A *LONG u* SPELLING

A sufffix can be added to any of these *long u* spellings without any spelling alteration.
Example:

cool + er	=	cooler
few + er	=	fewer
argue + ment	=	arguement
suit + able	=	suitable

EXCEPT:
Remove the *silent e* from the end of a *u - e* and *ue* spelling when you are adding a vowel suffix that can do the job of the *silent e*.
Example:

	argue + ing	=	arguing
	argue + ed	=	argued
BUT	argue + ment	=	arguement
	use + er	=	user
	use + ing	=	using
BUT	use + ful	=	useful

PRACTICE : THE *LONG u* SOUND

> There are three ways of spelling a *long u* sound:
>
> **1. Add *e* to the end of the word which follows the pattern *u - e*.**
> **2. In the middle of a word with another vowel: *oo* or *ou*
>   (and sometimes *ui*).**
> **3. At the end of the word use *ew* or *ue*.**

Exercise Thirty-Four: _____

Copy each word saying aloud the letters as you do so. Put a circle around all the *long u* spellings.

glue	_____	nephew	_____	blew	_____	youth	_____
view	_____	group	_____	choose	_____	bruise	_____
screw	_____	rule	_____	juice	_____	brew	_____
blue	_____	soup	_____	school	_____	true	_____
cruise	_____	crew	_____	cube	_____	chew	_____
knew	_____	drew	_____	stoop	_____	broom	_____
hue	_____	queue	_____	refuse	_____	coupon	_____
acute	_____	consume	_____	pursue	_____	rebuke	_____

THE *oo* SPELLING

The *oo* spelling can make two different sounds:

long u   as in moon, stoop, cool, stool
short u   as in book, look, cook, wood

Exercise Thirty-Five: _____

Copy, saying these words aloud as you do so. Place a macron above a *long u* sound, and a breve above a *short u* sound.

book	_____	fool	_____	groove	_____	bloom	_____
soot	_____	brook	_____	hook	_____	moon	_____
stoop	_____	spool	_____	scoop	_____	good	_____
tooth	_____	stood	_____	wool	_____	choose	_____
crook	_____	goose	_____	school	_____	look	_____
cook	_____	wood	_____	blood	_____	food	_____
spoon	_____	doom	_____	flood	_____	took	_____
mood	_____	pool	_____	cool	_____	tool	_____
hood	_____	nook	_____	zoom	_____	hoop	_____

Exercise Thirty-Six: _____

Put *u - e, oo, ou, ui, ew* or *ue* into these words so the *u* is *long*. Each gap says *long u*. When you have finished, mark the Exercise and copy each word carefully saying aloud each letter as you do so. Then, when you are ready, cover over each word and try to rewrite it from memory.

c__b__   _____ _____   sh__t   _____ _____

bl__(colour)   _____ _____   bl__(puffed)   _____ _____

thr__   _____ _____   gr__p   _____ _____

l__t   _____ _____   sch__l   _____ _____

c__pon   _____ _____   vi__   _____ _____

neph__   _____ _____   tr__p   _____ _____

sc__p   _____ _____   kn__   _____ _____

d__(moisture)   _____ _____   d__(expected) _____ _____

br__se   _____ _____   ref__s__   _____ _____

que__   _____ _____   j__ce   _____ _____

Exercise Thirty-Seven: _____

Some words with a *long u* sound can be spelt in two different ways to give two different meanings. These words are called *homophones*. Can you put these words into the correct sentence? Use a dictionary if you need one.

blew blue
    The wind _____ through the trees.
    She was wearing a pretty _____ dress.

through threw
    He _____ the ball in the air.
    The car drove _____ the tunnel at speed.

root route
    In the mist, he took the wrong _____ and got lost.
    The tree _____ was visible, overhanging the stream.

choose chews
    The child _____ her food noisily.
    She found it difficult to _____ a new book.

dew due
    The cricket match was cancelled _____ to the poor weather.
    The morning _____ was still on the lawn when we left the house.

queue cue
    The actor missed his _____ and fell silent.
    There was an endless _____ of cars waiting to enter the car park.

THE *LONG e* SOUND

There are three ways of spelling a *long e* sound:

1. By putting an *e* on the end of a word which follows the pattern *e - e*.
Example:

the s e	=	these
supre m e	=	supreme
comple t e	=	complete
extre m e	=	extreme

2. In the middle of a word, when *e* is immediately followed by another vowel, usually another *e* or *a* (and more unusually *i*, as in *protein*), the *e* will be *long*.
Example:

st ee p	=	steep
br ee ze	=	breeze
str ee t	=	street
r ea ch	=	reach
cl ea r	=	clear
p ea ch	=	peach

NOTE: There is no guiding rule to help correct spelling here, only visual memory.

3. *Ey* at the end of a word says *long e*.*
Example:

vall ey	=	valley
hock ey	=	hockey
troll ey	=	trolley

*ey at the end of a word can also say *ay*.
Example:

survey

convey

To avoid confusion, I shall only use *ey* spellings which make a *long e* sound for the purposes of these Exercises.

ADDING A SUFFIX TO A *LONG e* SPELLING

A suffix can be added to any of the *long e* spellings without any spelling alteration.

Example:

cheer + ful	=	cheerful
reach + es	=	reaches
clear + ing	=	clearing

EXCEPT:
Remove the *silent e* from the end of an *e - e* spelling when you are adding a vowel suffix that can do the job of the *silent e*.
Example:

complete + ing   =   completing
recede + ed   =   receded

BUT   extreme + ly   =   extremely

PRACTICE : THE *LONG e* SOUND

There are three ways of spelling a *long e* sound:

1. **Add *e* to the end of a word which follows the pattern *e - e*.**
2. ***e* immediately followed by another *e* or an *a* (and sometimes *i*) in the middle of the word says *long e*.**
3. **Use *ey* at the end of the word.**

Exercise Thirty-Eight: _____

These words have an *ey* or *e-e* spelling for the *long e* sound. Copy each word saying the letters aloud as you do so. Put a circle around the *long e* spelling.

donkey	_____	pulley	_____	hockey	_____	whiskey	_____
jersey	_____	valley	_____	barley	_____	kidney	_____
turkey	_____	alley	_____	volley	_____	trolley	_____
supreme	_____	concrete	_____	excrete	_____	Terylene	_____
polythene	_____	complete	_____	intervene	_____	secrete	_____
impede	_____	extreme	_____	Crimplene	_____	acetylene	_____

Exercise Thirty-Nine:_____

Which of the *long e* words in Exercise Thirty-Eight are the names of man-made fibres?

_____

Use each of the following four words in sentences of your own so that the meaning of each word is clear from the way you have used it. A dictionary may help.

impede   intervene   excrete   secrete

_____

_____

THE *ea* SPELLING

The *ea* spelling can make two different *e* sounds:
> *long e*   as in r*ea*l, s*ea*l, p*ea*ce, cl*ea*r
> *short e*   as in l*ea*ther, w*ea*ther, f*ea*ther

Exercise Forty: _____

These words spelt with *ea,* say *short e*. Copy, saying each letter aloud as you do so. Put a circle around the *short e* spelling.

lead	_____	deaf	_____	meant	_____	treasure	_____
measure	_____	instead	_____	heaven	_____	dealt	_____
sweat	_____	pleasure	_____	dead	_____	healthy	_____
bread	_____	jealous	_____	spread	_____	threat	_____
dread	_____	meadow	_____	already	_____	feather	_____

Exercise Forty-One: _____

These words spelt with *ea* all say *long e*. Copy, saying aloud each letter as you do so. Put a circle around the *long e* spelling.

beach	_____	reach	_____	flea	_____	clear	_____
read	_____	tea	_____	each	_____	fear	_____
ear	_____	heat	_____	reason	_____	steal	_____
heal	_____	defeat	_____	hear	_____	peace	_____
dream	_____	steam	_____	beam	_____	stream	_____
nearly	_____	greasy	_____	league	_____	ideal	_____
creature	_____	disease	_____	eagle	_____	treacle	_____
weave	_____	really	_____	wheat	_____	shears	_____
fearless	_____	wearily	_____	beaker	_____	unbeatable	_____

Exercise Forty-Two: _____

Copy, saying these words aloud as you do so. Place a *macron* above a *long e* sound, and a *breve* above a *short e* sound.

wear	_____	leave	_____	dream	_____	leather	_____

weapon _____ learn _____ cream _____ pear _____

weather_____ each _____ instead _____ cheap _____

ease _____ heavy _____ neat _____ heather_____

breath _____ weave _____ beneath_____ ready _____

Exercise Forty-Three: _____

These words all say *long e*. Copy each word, saying aloud the letters as you do so. Put a circle around all the *long e* spellings.

sweet _____ donkey _____ honey _____ valley _____

complete _____ cheese _____ easy _____ these _____

money _____ peanut _____ cheat _____ jockey _____

mean _____ speed _____ steel _____ cheer _____

kidney _____ serene _____ extreme_____ sneak _____

Exercise Forty-Four: _____

Put *e - e*, *ee*, *ea* and *ey* into these words so the *e* is *long*. Each gap says *long e*. When you have finished, mark the Exercise and copy each word carefully, saying aloud each letter as you do so. Then, cover over each word and try to rewrite it from memory.

pull____ _____ _____ str____t _____ _____

ch____r _____ _____ cl____r _____ _____

troll____ _____ _____ sp____d _____ _____

sp____r _____ _____ hon____ _____ _____

vall____ _____ _____ th____s____ _____ _____

b____ch(tree) _____ _____ b____ch(sandy) _____ _____

st____p _____ _____ secr____t____ _____ _____

chimn____ _____ _____ mon____ _____ _____

sn____k _____ _____ compl____t____ _____ _____

l____ve _____ _____ concr____t____ _____ _____

RULE SUMMARIES

Here you are asked to do three things:
1. Read through all the Rules that have been identified in this book, one at a time.
2. When you are ready, fill in the missing words in the Rule Summaries below.
3. Explain in your own words what is meant by each Rule, making reference to the examples given.

THE DOUBLING RULE

Read through **THE DOUBLING RULE** on pages 2 to 4. When you are ready, complete the following Rule Summary without referring to that section.

A vowel will always be *short* and says its *sound* unless we do something to it.

To keep the _____ sound of a vowel, there are usually ___ _____ between the _____ vowel and the next _____. To achieve this we may have to do something to the word.
1. We may need to _____ the _____ consonant before adding a _____ which begins with a vowel.
2. Simply add the _____ if it begins with a _____.
3. Do _____ if there are already ___ _____ following the _____ vowel in the ____ word, or if there is a vowel _____ making a ____ _____ sound. In this case there is no longer a _____ _____ to protect.

Now turn back to the **DOUBLING RULE** on page 4 and check your answers.

KEEPING YOUR OWN RECORD OF THE SPELLING RULES IN THESE BOOKS

To keep a permanent record of the Spelling Rules in these Books - a record to which you can refer at any time - you need a pack of 5ins x 8ins index cards and an index card box or A5 file.

CARD ONE:
Take an index card and copy the **DOUBLING RULE** from the top of page 4 carefully and clearly on the first side of the Card. Spread out your writing so it is not crammed, but is neat and easy to read.

On the reverse side of Card One:
1. Using the following Examples, explain in your own words what exactly is meant by **The Doubling Rule**.

    Example:

fat + *t* + est	and	hid + *d* + en
	but	
hot + ly	and	jump + ed

2. Make your own notes about doubling the *final letter of a word of more than one syllable*. Using the Examples from page 6, explain precisely when the final letter is doubled and when it is not.

CARD TWO:
Read the Rules concerning the *123* **RULE** on pages 9 and 10. When you are ready, complete the following Rule Summary without referring to that section.

The *123* RULE

Words of ONE _____ with ONE _____ _____ ending in -l -s -f and -k sound
end in -___ -___ -___ and -___ ,

EXCEPT:

If there are two _____ , or one _____ plus a _____ in the ____ word, in which
case use ___, ___ and ___.

Turn back to the *123* **RULE** on page 10 and check your answers.

Take another 5ins x 8ins index card and copy carefully, clearly and neatly the *123* **RULE** from page 10.

On the reverse side of Card Two, answer the following question:
What does the *123* **Rule** mean? Explain fully in your own words. Copy and use these examples to help.
Examples:

		123	123	123	123
	A	sail	cool	beak	leaf

This is an example of _____ + _____ + l, k or f.

		123	123	123	123
	B	talk	bark	girl	calf

This is an example of _____ + _____ + l, k or f.

Copy: This is known as the __ __ __ Rule which states that there are always 3 letters from the _____
vowel to the ___ of the word.

CARD THREE:
COPY onto side one of Card Three:

To keep a vowel short it is necessary to 'protect' it with two consonants. These have
the effect of 'blocking' the effect of another vowel which may follow and stopping it
making the first vowel long.

Record any word in Exercises One to Eight on pages 4 to 12 which have a short vowel followed by a
double consonant and which you find particularly useful to remember. Try to learn these words.

On the reverse of Card Three, make a note of any SPELLING EXCEPTIONS where a vowel retains its
short sound even though it is followed by a single consonant.

CARD FOUR:
Read through the notes concerning **THE *SILENT* e RULE** on pages 13 to 15. When you are ready,
complete the following Rule Summary without referring to that section.

An *e* on the end of a word makes the _____ say its____.

If we add a _____ which begins with a _____ that can do the job of the *silent* ___ ,
then the ___ can be _____. If, however, you are adding a _____ which begins with
a _____, the ___ must_____.
The *silent e* does not make any sound, it merely has a job to do.

Check your answer by referring to the **SILENT e RULE** on page 15. Then, onto the first side of Card
Four copy the **SILENT e RULE** from page 15.

On the reverse of Card Four, answer the following question:
A *silent e* makes a vowel *long* and so say its *name*. When we add a suffix we sometimes drop the *e* and
sometimes keep it. Explain. Use these Examples to help.
Example:

tire + ed and drive + er and stone + y

but

wise + ly and tire + some and care + less

CARD FIVE:

Read the Rules concerning **THE y RULE** on pages 18 and 19. When you are ready, complete the
following Rule Summary without referring to that section.

When adding a _____ to a word which ends in __, the __ is always changed to an __.

EXCEPT:

1. When the *y* has a _____ immediately ___ _____ of it.
2. When the *y* has an ___ immediately _____ it.

Check your answer by referring to **THE y RULE** on page 19. Copy **THE y RULE** onto the first side of
Card Five.

On the reverse of Card Five, explain the Rule in your own words using the following Examples.

heavy	+	ness
melody	+	ous
lazy	+	ly
play	+	ing
joy	+	ful
enjoy	+	able
spy	+	ing
worry	+	ing
cry	+	ing

WAYS OF SPELLING THE LONG VOWEL SOUNDS

CARD SIX:

Read the Rules concerning **THE LONG a SOUND** on pages 20 and 21. When you are ready, complete
the following Rule Summary without referring to that section.

There are _____ ways of spelling a *long a* sound.
1. Add ___ to the ___ of a word which follows the pattern _____.
2. Put another _____ (usually ___) immediately _____ the *a*.
3. Use _____ at the end of a word.

Now turn back to the **LONG a SOUND** on page 21 and check your answer. Copy the **LONG a RULE** onto the first side of Card Six.

On the reverse of Card Six explain in your own words what spelling alterations have to be made when adding a suffix to a *long a* spelling.(Refer to page 24.) Use these examples to help you:

$$
\begin{array}{rcl}
\text{skate} + \text{ing} & = & \text{skating} \\
\text{state} + \text{ment} & = & \text{statement} \\
\text{decay} + \text{ing} & = & \text{decaying} \\
\text{train} + \text{ing} & = & \text{training} \\
\text{stain} + \text{less} & = & \text{stainless}
\end{array}
$$

CARD SEVEN:

Read through the rules concerning the **LONG i SOUND** on pages 25 and 26, then without referring to that section, complete the following Rule Summary:

There are _____ ways of spelling the *long i* sound.
1. Add ___ to the ____ of a word which follows the pattern ____.
2. When *i* is followed by ___, the *i* will be long.
3. Use ___ or ___ at the ____ of a word.

Read page 26 to check your answers and then copy the Rules concerning the **LONG i SOUND** onto the first side of Card Seven.

On the reverse side of Card Seven complete the following:
1. Explain what spelling alterations have to be made when a suffix is added to a *long i* spelling (page 26).
2. Explain why a *y* on the end of a word is sometimes pronounced as a *short i*, and sometimes as a *long i*.

CARD EIGHT:

Read the rules concerning **THE LONG o SOUND** on pages 28 and 29 and when you are ready complete the following Rule summary without referring to that section.

There are _____ ways of spelling the *long o* sound.
1. Add ____ to the ____ of a word which follows the pattern ____.
2. When *o* is followed by _____ _____, usually ___, the *o* will be long.
3. Use ____ or ____ at the ___ of a word.

Read through the Rule on page 29 and check your answers. Copy the Rule concerning the **LONG o SOUND** onto the first side of Card Eight.

On the reverse side of Card Eight complete the following:
1. Explain what spelling alterations need to be made when a suffix is added to a *long o* spelling.
2. Explain in your own words what these examples are trying to illustrate:

hoe + ed = hoed	BUT	hoe + ing = hoeing
woe + ed = woed	BUT	woe + ing = woeing
hope + ed = hoped	AND	hope + ing = hoping

3. What is a *homophone*?

CARD NINE:

Read through the notes concerning **THE LONG u SOUND** on pages 32 and 33 and when you are ready complete the following Rule Summary without referring to that section.

There are _____ ways of spelling a *long u* sound.
1. Add ____ to the end of a word which follows the pattern ____.
2. In the _____ of a word with another _____: ___ or ___ and sometimes ___.
3. At the ____ of a word: ____ or ____.

Read page 33 to check your answers. Then copy this Rule onto the first side of Card Nine.

On the reverse side of Card Nine:
1. Explain what spelling alterations have to be made when a suffix is added to a *long u* spelling.
2. What are the two sound the *oo* spelling can make and give examples?

CARD TEN:
Read pages 36 and 37 concerning **THE *LONG e* SOUND** and when you are ready complete the following Rule summary without referring to that section.

There are _____ ways of spelling the *long e* sound.
1. Add ____ to the ____ of the word which follows the pattern ____.
2. ____ immediately followed by another ____, an ____ and sometimes ____ in the _____ of a word says *long e*.
3. Use ____ at the ____ of the word.

Check your answer by referring back to page 37. Copy onto the first side of Card Ten the above Rule.

On the reverse side of Card Ten explain:
1. What spelling alterations have to be made when a suffix is added to a *long e* spelling.
2. What two different *e* sounds are made by *ea*. Give examples to illustrate your answer.

CARDS ELEVEN and TWELVE:
Make a note of any of the words in Book One which you have found difficult to remember and which you need to look at again. Alongside each word, make a note of the Rule to which it belongs, and a page reference, so you can look it up and read over the Rule again. Try to learn these words. Set out your Card like this:

Words I have found difficult to remember in Book One and which I need to look at again.

WORD	RULE	PAGE	LEARNT

ANSWERS

Working *down* the Exercises, the Answers are as follows:

Exercise 1
neatest, sipping, madness, dusty, gripping, witty, meeting, hotly, helper, painful, fatness, biggest, pegging, redder, flattest, hidden, rusty, planning, jumped, risky

Exercise 2
grinning, banking, sunny, rubbed, funny, beggar, floppy, skinny, gladly

Exercise 3
dragged, harden, badly, slimmed, luggage, coldness, fretful, harder, wooden, stopping, sleeping, jammed, crispy, jagged, farming, starry, stabbed, floppy, rotten

swimming, shutter, waiter, shouting, shipment, chipping, bashful, milked, goodness, tripped, reddish, grinning

Exercise 5
fool, well, snail, meal, pull, curl, mill, girl, pool, feel, snarl, hurt, will, pail, tall, tool, tail, cell, heel, dull, scarf, sniff, proof, cliff, hoof, self, roof, calf, ruff

half, beef, muff, stuff, leaf, stiff, loaf, bluff, reef, grief, aloof, clock, back, think, deck, desk, jerk, luck, park, leak, wreck, lick, junk, bank, book, suck, slick, crack, cook, bleak, tank

Exercise 6
sitting, dressing, barking, shipment, crossing, guessed, dizzy, rubbish, dimmer, sniffed, parked, swimming, gladly, puffing, buzzer, passage, hidden, fitment

sniffing, fuller, kneeling, sadness, surfing, twirled, milking, wrapped, sailing, spoiled, flatten

Exercise 7
fossil, harass, lesson, mistress, necessary, passage, passenger, possess, process, progress, success

cloaked, missed, fitment, banking, slipped, capful, sweater, patted, madly, selling, bandage

Exercise 10
accessible, actress, address, aggressive, confess, distress, embarrass

Exercise 11
address, passage, harass, necessary, possess, distress, lesson, success, confess, progress

Exercise 13
baking, tiresome, bony, careful, smoky, wiser, biting, taking, placing, priceless, famous, blamed, hopeful, wider, likely, likeable, tuneless, spicy, shiny

joker

Exercise 14
ripeness, writing, safety, taped, sloping, hiding, faded, closeness, grateful, homeless, amazement, shameful, gravely, timely, amusement, shady, hateful, smiling, lazy, rosy

Exercise 15
cuteness, rated, lonesome, skating, driver, quotation, debatable

wasteful
cutest
tiresome
hopeful
hateful
deserving
pavement
multiplied
employment
joyful
homely
shapely
spiteful
placing
easily
glorious
copying
supplied
advisable
educator
gravity
worrying
envious
blameless
distasteful
payment
invitation
annoyed
shaken
brayed
ageless
shameless
uniting
refusal
useful
careless
grimy

Exercise 16
spying
prayer
crattiness
crying
heaviness
buyer
readiness
daily
enjoyable
noisiest

melodious
steadiness
carrying
happiness
enjoyment
multiplied
employment
joyful
glorious
copying
easily

Exercise 17
lonely + ness
rely + able
hurry + ed
worry + ed
mystery + ous
dismay + ed
day + ly
easy + ly
supply + er
employ + ment

cry + ing
joy + ful
happy + ness
fury + ous
duty + ful
heavy + ness
ready + ness

enjoy + ment
smoky + ness
marry + ing
key + s
annoy + ance
jolly + est
melody + ous
today
tried
tied
frying
tighten
happy + er
crafty + ness
envy + ous

Exercise 20
1. maid made
2. pale pail
3. main mane
4. mail male
5. pain pane
6. sale sail

Exercise 22
displayed
management
paintbrush
tracing
straining
mistaking
explaining
skating

Chandler - dealer in
ropes, canvas and other
supplies for ships.
Also dealer in candles.
Homophone - a word
which sounds the same
as another but which
has a different meaning
and may have a
different spelling.

dismayed
paint
claim
manage
holiday
Britain
train
explain
dying

snail
tray
display
skate
slate
slay
frying
tighten

Exercise 24
plight
fright
surprise
lying
knight
slightly
dryer
frightened
shyly

Exercise 21
railway
pail
grain
mountain
mistake
birthday

wine
lied
drying
nightmare

Exercise 26
1. sighed sight
2. might mite
3. size excitement
4. spy tried fly tie sky
5. sight bright kite
night sky delighted

Exercise 29
loaf
soap
know
throat
goal
hope
narrow
afloat
fellow

Exercise 32
soak
oak
soap
roast
goal
throat
coal
float
toast
foal
elbow

snow
follow
coal
elbow
slope
elbow

Exercise 30
1. elbow
2. boat road
3. mare foal
4. below
5. coal snow
6. tall slow

Exercise 31
1. SNOW
2. GLOW
3. POLE
4. ROSE
5. COAT
6. HOPE
7. SLOW
8. ROLE

group
school
view
troop
knew
due
refuse
juice

Exercise 37
blew blue
threw through
route root
chews choose
due dew
cue queue

Exercise 36
cube
blue

Exercise 39
Crimplene
Terylene

Exercise 44
pulley
trolley
cheer
spear
valley
beech
steep

coupon
nephew
scoop
dew
bruise
queue
shoot
blew
honey
these
beach
secrete
money
complete
concrete

chimney
sneak
leave
street
clear
speed
honey
these
beach
secret